The Hungry Snake

BY SUZANNE HOBBS

PAGE PUBLISHING, INC.
New York, NY

First originally published by Page Publishing, Inc. 2016

ISBN 978-1-68213-381-1 (pbk)
ISBN 978-1-68213-382-8 (digital)

Printed in the United States of America

This book is dedicated to my daughter, Lilly Love.
Thank you for inspiring me to tell stories.

Once upon a time there was a snake and he was hungry, but he didn't know what to eat.

So he started slithering through the grass and he came upon a horse and said, "Horse, I'm a snake and I'm hungry what should I eat?"

The horse said, "Well, horses eat hay.
If you'd like to try some of my hay, help yourself."

The snake gave the hay a few bites and said, "Hmmmm. That's not too bad, but it's not what snakes eat. Thanks anyway!"

And the hungry snake slithered
away through the grass.

Then he came upon a rooster and he said,
"Rooster, I'm a snake and
I'm hungry what should I eat?"

The rooster said, "Well, roosters eat corn. If you'd like to try some of my yellow corn, help yourself."

The snake ate a few kernels of corn and said, "Hmmmm. That's pretty tasty, but it's not what snakes eat. Thanks anyway!"

By now, the snake was getting really hungry.

His long snake tummy was growling as he
slithered through the tall, soft grass.

Then he came upon a brown bear sitting next to a tree stump. The bear was licking his sticky paws. He said, "Bear, I'm a snake and I'm hungry, what should I eat?"

The furry bear said, "Bears love to eat honey. I'll share mine with you." And the bear let the hungry snake's tongue lick some sweet honey from his paw.

He thought for a minute and said, "Hmmmm. That is delicious and sweet, but that's not what snakes eat. Thanks anyway!"

11

And by now, this snake was more than just hungry, he was VERY hungry!

He carried on and as he slithered through the grass, he came upon a grasshopper laying in the warm sun and he said, "Grasshopper, I'm a snake and I'm very hungry, what should I eat?"

The grasshopper thought for a
moment and said, "Well...."
And the snake went...

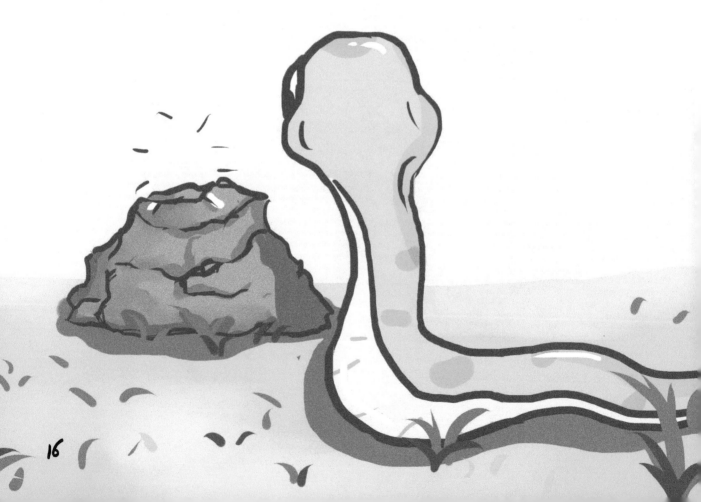

And he wasn't hungry anymore.

THE END

About the Author

Suzanne Hobbs has been a story teller since she was a young girl growing up in Idaho. There are hours of home movies of her reporting on family events with the home movie camera. That passion turned in to a career when she was 22 years old and was hired as a television reporter in her home state.

She worked for nearly 14 years as a reporter and news anchor; specializing in court and crime cases for both NBC and CBS affiliate stations in Idaho. It was a career she truly loved.

One significant story Suzanne covered was in October 2000. A tragic story led her to advocate for a Safe Haven Law in Idaho. That law (now in all 50 states) allows for birth mothers to safely surrender their newborn babies to "safe places" like hospitals, fire stations, and places of worship.

In 2003 Suzanne adopted her first and only child, who happened to be a newborn who was safely surrendered at a hospital under the protection of the law she helped implement. Her powerful story has been told in several magazines, two books, on television, radio, and she even appeared as a guest on *The Oprah Winfrey Show*. Suzanne also does public speaking about her story and is an educator on the Baby Safe Haven Laws.

She has lived most of her life in eastern Idaho, but has also lived in Pittsburgh, Pennsylvania and now lives in South Carolina.

Follow Suzanne on Facebook and Instagram @suzannehobbs365 or visit her website at www.suzannehobbs.com.

Order more copies of *The Hungry Snake* at www.thehungrysnake.com and follow *The Hungry Snake* on Facebook and Instagram @thehungrysnakebook.

Learn more about the Safe Haven Law at www.nationalsafehavenalliance.org.

CPSIA information can be obtained
at www.ICGtesting.com
Printed in the USA
BVHW090941031218
534641BV00016B/1229/P